THE EXTRAORDINARY WORLD OF

Fred

The Extraordinary World of Fred is the third compilation of cartoons featuring Fred, the suburban hero of the nineties. Since the publication of **More Fred**, much has happened to Fred, Penelope and their friends. Their wit and wisdom has found it's way onto a popular range of T-shirts, and their greeting cards continue to spread the word. Following this success, plans are currently underway for Fred to make his way onto television.

Statics (London) Ltd
41 Standard Road, London NW10 6HF

First published by Statics 1992

© 1992 by Rupert Fawcett

Printed in England by H.P.H. Print Ltd
8 Gorst Road, London NW10 6LE.

ISBN 1-873922-02-7

THE EXTRAORDINARY WORLD OF
FRED

RUPERT FAWCETT

STATICS BOOKS

EVERYONE EAGERLY AWAITED A SLICE OF
PENELOPE'S UPSIDE-DOWN CAKE

FRED ALWAYS INSISTED ON
HELPING WITH THE GROCERIES

FRED THANKED BOB FOR THE
EXTRA PINT OF GOLD-TOP

WHEN IT CAME TO FRED'S BAD BACK
MR AND MRS NESBIT SEEMED TO
HAVE THE MAGIC TOUCH

PIP WAS BECOMING SUSPICIOUS
ABOUT FRED'S SO-CALLED
LUCKY STREAK

FRED LOVED TO CURL UP
WITH A GOOD BOOK

FRED COULD FORESEE A DAY WHEN EVERY HOUSEHOLD IN THE COUNTRY WOULD OWN ONE OF HIS 'EEZISHINE' PEDAL-POWERED SHOE BUFFERS

FRED ADORED COMPETITIONS

IT WAS PENELOPE'S NEW FRIENDS
FROM CHOCOHOLICS ANONYMOUS

DEEP DOWN INSIDE FRED FELT SURE
THAT IN SOME PREVIOUS LIFE HE HAD
BEEN A YELLOW-CRESTED TIT

PENELOPE'S FAVOURITE PARTY
GAME WAS CALLED 'SELF CONTROL'

'IVE GOT ONE IN EVERY ROOM`,
SAID FRED SHOWING OFF THE
EMERGENCY LOLLIPOP

PIP'S APPLICATION TO JOIN THE GENTLEMEN'S ZIG-ZAG CLUB WAS REJECTED DUE TO 'INSUFFICIENT VISIBLE ZIG-ZAGS'

'HANDS UP WHO LOVES ME',
COMMANDED PENELOPE

PIP HAD KNOWN THERE WOULD BE
A PRICE TO PAY FOR TAKING
FRED'S LAST HUMBUG

THE DENTAL FLOSS WAS
WELL AND TRULY STUCK

FRED OFTEN WONDERED WHY A GOOD-
LOOKING CHAP LIKE PENELOPE'S COUSIN
FRANK NEVER HAD ANY GIRLFRIENDS

FRED HAD BEEN WARNED ABOUT
LEAVING THE LAVATORY SEAT UP

PIP HAD EVIDENTLY BECOME INCREASINGLY
BORING DURING THE COURSE OF THE YEAR

IT WAS TIME FOR FRED TO HEAR
ABOUT THE BIRDS AND THE BEES

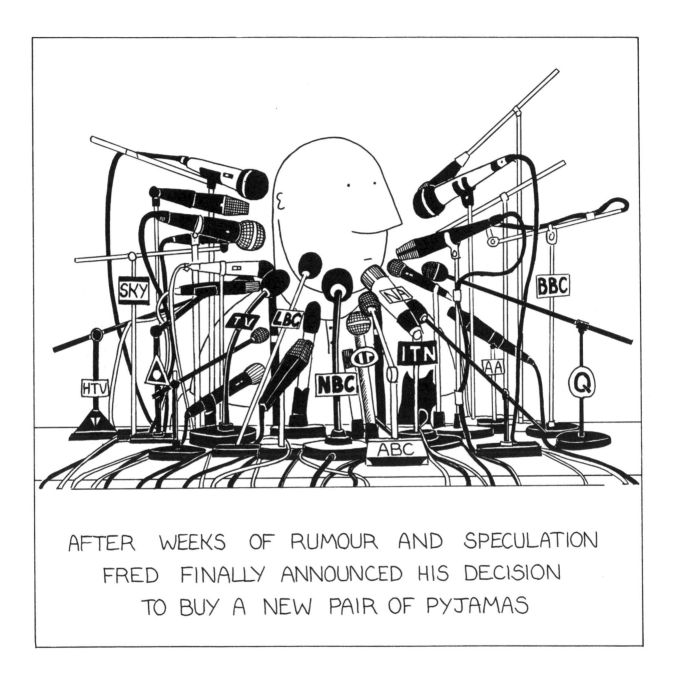

AFTER WEEKS OF RUMOUR AND SPECULATION
FRED FINALLY ANNOUNCED HIS DECISION
TO BUY A NEW PAIR OF PYJAMAS

FRED'S WAVE MACHINE TOOK THE EFFORT OUT OF FAREWELLS

THIS IS WHERE FRED KEEPS HIS
STAGE-GEAR REVEALED PENELOPE

PIP WAS FINALLY INITIATED INTO THE
SECRET TOMATO KETCHUP CLUB

FRED AND PENELOPE WERE BEGINNING
TO WISH THEY'D NEVER HEARD THE NAME
'CHEEKY BATHROOM MIRRORS INCORPORATED'

FRED LIKED TO THINK OF HIMSELF
AS AN ENTREPRENEUR

PENELOPE HAD FOUND
HER VOCATION

FRED COULDN'T HELP NOTICING THAT HIS
CAR WAS THE ONLY ONE IN THE STREET
TO SHRINK IN THE RAIN

FRED WAS ALWAYS REWARDED
FOR HELPING WITH THE GROCERIES

JEREMY SEEMED INTRIGUED BY
PENELOPE'S NOSE-JOB SUGGESTION

PENELOPE INSISTED THAT FRED GO
AND GET HIS HAIR CUT

FRED KNEW THAT IF HE COULD SIMPLY REDUCE THE SIZE OF HIS HEARING – AID INVENTION HE WOULD BE ON TO A WINNER

AS USUAL CHRISTMAS WAS
FRAUGHT WITH DRAMA

MR AND MRS NESBIT APOLOGISED TO FRED
FOR HAVING DOUBTED HIS GIANT CARDIGAN STORY

FRED HAD ALWAYS SUSPECTED THERE
WAS ANOTHER SIDE TO MRS NESBIT

PENELOPE KNEW EXACTLY WHERE
SHE WOULD LIKE FRED TO SHOVE
HIS GOLF CLUBS

FOR MONTHS AFTERWARDS FRED TORTURED
HIMSELF WITH THE SAME QUESTION;
COULD HE SOMEHOW HAVE AVOIDED
STEPPING ON THAT ANT?

FRED SHOWED OFF THE JEWEL IN
THE CROWN OF HIS CORNFLAKE COLLECTION,
A 1927 SLIGHTLY OVER-COOKED KELLOGG'S

FRED HAD HIS OWN PARTICULAR
WAY OF SAYING SORRY

IT WAS ANOTHER OF FRED'S
BOUNCY CASTLE DREAMS

PENELOPE WOULD HAVE PREFERRED
THE VALENTINE CARD WITHOUT
THE VALENTINE DANCE

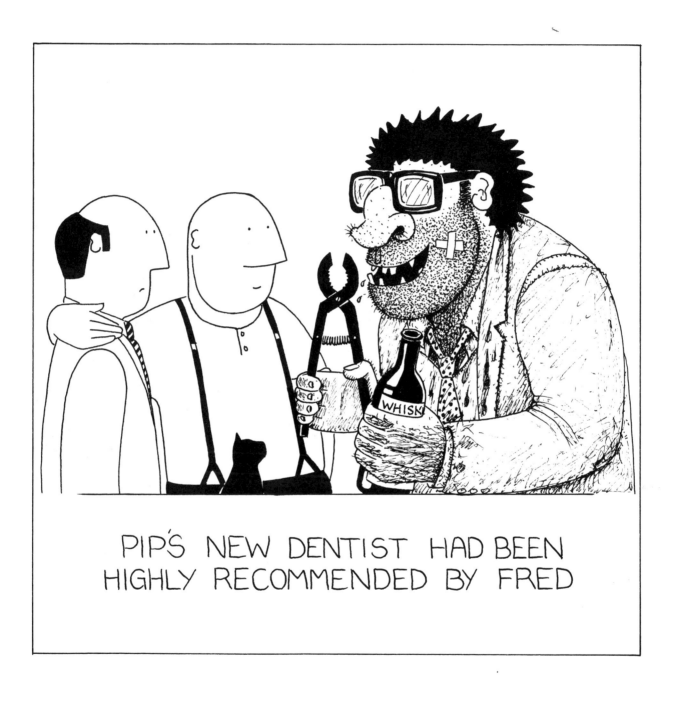

PIP'S NEW DENTIST HAD BEEN
HIGHLY RECOMMENDED BY FRED

FRED APPEARED TO HAVE MISPLACED
THE KEY TO HIS 'SAHARA SIMULATOR'

AFTER DINNER THE MEN
PLAYED POCKET BILLIARDS

PENELOPE'S DIET RESTRICTED HER TO JUST ONE MINCE PIE OVER CHRISTMAS

FRED WAS INVITED TO SPEAK AT
THE ANNUAL DINNER-DANCE OF
THE ROYAL GUILD OF NOSEPICKERS

PIP SEEMED UNIMPRESSED BY
FRED'S TROUSER-TEARING TRICK

FRED SHOWED MR AND MRS NESBIT
TO THE GUEST ROOM

FRED WAS FAMOUS FOR HIS
CHRISTMAS BARBECUES

PENELOPE WAS INTRIGUED BY
THE CONTENTS OF FRED'S WARDROBE

FRED FOUND HIS NEW CAREER
IMMENSELY REWARDING

FRED AND PENELOPE HAD VARIOUS WAYS OF
DECIDING WHO WOULD DO THE WASHING UP

FRED ALWAYS LIKED TO GET
AWAY AT CHRISTMAS

PIP WAS EXPERIENCING DIFFICULTY
KEEPING UP WITH THE LATEST FASHIONS

PIP GENEROUSLY AGREED TO
LEND FRED FIFTY PENCE

FRED WAS READY FOR
THE CAROL SINGERS

FRED COULD HAPPILY SPEND ALL DAY
JUST WATCHING THE WORLD GO BY